Yuck & Yum
A Feast of Funny Food Poems

Poems by Joshua Seigal and Neal Zetter

Illustrations by Scoular Anderson

troika

Published by TROIKA

First published 2018

1 3 5 7 9 10 8 6 4 2

Poems by Joshua Seigal (JS) Text copyright © Joshua Seigal 2018
Poems by Neal Zetter (NZ) Text copyright © Neal Zetter 2018
Illustrations copyright © Scoular Anderson 2018
The moral rights of the authors and illustrator have been asserted

A CIP catalogue record for this book
is available from the British Library

ISBN 978-1-909991-45-3

Printed in Poland

Troika Books Ltd
Well House, Green Lane, Ardleigh CO7 7PD, UK
www.troikabooks.com

Mealtime

Breakfast

What do you do when you get out of bed
And you have a dry throat and you have a sore head
And you feel like one of the living dead?
Have breakfast.

It's a plate of fuel for the rest of your day
It's a bowl of power for work, rest and play
You wouldn't have it any other way —
It's breakfast.

If you don't eat it you'll feel all grouchy
You'll feel all shuffly, you'll feel all slouchy
So shovel it in your little pouchy —
Have breakfast.

It's porridge! It's toast! It's a blueberry muffin!
I'll tell you one thing and I'll tell you for nothin' —
Your belly is empty, you need to get stuffin'!
No more huffin'!
No more puffin'!
(Although they do eat puffin in Greenland...)
HAVE BREAKFAST!

(This poem was brought to you by
the National Breakfast Association)

Joshua Seigal

Dodgy Food Fact

The National Breakfast Association (NBA) was an
organisation set up in Lithuania in 1822 to promote
breakfast. Before that, people used to wait until lunch
before eating. They would frequently faint through hunger.

7

Don't Eat the Animals

Don't boil a bat
Don't bake a snake
Don't microwave a millipede
Don't cook koala cake

Don't grill a gorilla
Don't gnaw on a macaw
Never fry a fruit fly
Don't even have it raw

Don't coddle a cockroach
Don't fricassee a frog
Don't poach piranhas, ants, iguanas
Tapirs and hogs

Don't chomp on a chicken
Don't chew a kangaroo
Munching mandrills for a snack
Is not the thing to do

Don't steam a sea bass
Don't barbecue a bear
Don't serve a salamander
Medium rare

Don't pickle a penguin
Don't try terrapins on toast
Don't liquidise lynx for smoothie drinks
Don't make a rhino roast

Don't sauté a salmon
Don't catch a crab to crunch
Because the zoo will disappear
If you eat it for lunch

Neal Zetter

Dodgy Food Fact

Of all the animals listed in this poem the rhino is
the only one to have played for a Premiership
football team (Everton, 2010-12).

Pancake Day

Good morning, Mum and Dad,
and what a bright and sunny day!
We knew you would be hungry
so here's breakfast on a tray.

We thought we'd cook you pancakes
and our plan has not one glitch in:
they'll give you lots of energy
so you can clean the kitchen.

JS

Perfect Pancake Recipe

Buy a cake
Put it in a pan.

Poetry Perfected

Scottish poet and novelist Robert Louis Stevenson once stated, "Wine is bottled poetry." And that got me thinking...

A fine wine is poetry bottled
Beef dumplings are poetry stewed
Cool spring water is poetry pure and unspoilt
Jasmine tea is poetry gently brewed

BLT is poetry sandwiched
Blue Stilton is poetry matured very old
Fluffed scrambled eggs are poetry microwaved
Vanilla ice cream is poetry cold

French bread is poetry served straight from the oven
Buttered new potatoes are poetry boiled
Fresh garlic is poetry mushed and crushed
Dark chocolate is poetry unfoiled

English apples are poetry crunched
Barbecued burgers are poetry bapped
Real Italian cappuccino is poetry frothed
(Fast food isn't poetry it's just gangsta rap)

Scotch salmon is poetry smoked
Hot Welsh rarebit is poetry on toast
Red cherries and strawberries are poetry ripened
But poetry perfected is Mum's Sunday roast

NZ

Dodgy Food Fact

In Stone Age times the favoured meat for a Sunday roast was mammoth closely followed in popularity by sabre-toothed tiger.

Lost

I'm in the supermarket
And recoil with alarm
As I realise my hand has detached
From my mother's arm.
My head is spinning wildly
My eyes are darting round
I'm looking down the aisles
And she's nowhere to be found!
I look in the veggie section
And among the frozen goods
I survey the meat counter
And I scrutinise the puds.
I peer among confectionery
She's very much still missing
So I look among the sausages
The liver and the chicken.
I open the crisp packets
And I glance between the drinks
But she isn't there, or anywhere,
So I sit down and think:
It seems that I am lost for good
At least, that is my hunch
But as long as I am stuck in here
I think I'll have my lunch!

JS

Dodgy Food Fact

This actually happened to Joshua. He really did get lost in a supermarket, when he was 27 years old. He sometimes breaks down crying when performing this poem.

Literary Menu

Charles Chickens

William Hakespeare

Agatha Crispy

Roald Dhal

Dr Juice

Enid Pieton

JS

Dodgy Food Fact

Charles Chickens was a Victorian novelist, best known for his book *Great Eggspectations*.

International

One Ate

18, 21, 22
36, 39, 43

Were these my lucky numbers for the lottery today?
No, this was my dinner from the Chinese takeaway

NZ

Dodgy Food Fact

The world's first Chinese takeaway opened
not in China but in Iceland in 1406.

Hot Stuff

There's a hole in the plate
A hole in the mat
A hole in the table
Scorched fur on the cat

My trousers are burning
My throat is ablaze
The pot used for cooking
Now disintegrates

A hole's in the carpet
And on the stone floor
A window has blown out
We've lost the front door

The fire brigade's coming
The flames can't be stopped
'Cause Mum's piri-piri chicken was...
Hot! Hot! Hot!

NZ

Recipe Tip: Piri-Piri Chicken Variation
To make Mum's Piri-Piri chicken a bit cooler pour molten
lava over it from the nearest live volcano you can find.

Mexican Rap

I'm making a fajita
There's no neater treat to eat
Don't forget to get some lettuce
And some juicy strips of meat
Pack the cheese and pinto beans
With expertise, then start to dream
When the sauce resembles embers
Please remember sour cream
And I say

Yo! Fajita!
Yo! Yo! Fajita-jita!
Yo! Fajita!
Yo! Yo! Fajita-jita!

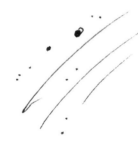

1, 2, 3, 4

I'm making enchiladas
With fresh peppers by the bunch
Get some nachos and gazpacho
It's a macho kind of lunch
I've a yearning for some burning
I'm discerning with my spice
And the chicken has me lickin'
As it sits upon the rice
And I say

En! Chilada!
En! En! Chilada-lada!
En! Chilada!
En! En! Chilada-lada!

1, 2, 3, 4

I'm making a burrito
Let me teach you how to scoff
Roll it tight with all your might
And then the night just might take off
Get your mother and your brother
And your uncle and your aunt
Plant them all across the table
And then listen as they chant
And they say

Yo! Burrito!
Yo! Yo! Burrito-rito!
Yo! Burrito!
Yo! Yo! Burrito-rito!
En! Chilada!
En! En! Chilada-lada!
En! Chilada!
En! En! Chilada-lada!

Yo! Fajita!
Yo! Yo! Fajita-jita!
Yo! Fajita!
Yo! Yo! Fajita-jita!

1, 2, 3, 4

Mmmmmmmmmmmmmmm!

JS

Human Fajita Recipe
Go into your parents' room
Wrap them up in the duvet
Add hot sauce (optional).

19

Claude le Croissant

Je m'appelle Claude le Croissant
The alternative to bread
Why bore yourself with sandwiches?
Just purchase me instead

Je m'appelle Claude le Croissant
For your breakfast, lunch or tea
My body shape's a crescent moon
Or like the letter "c"

You can stuff me with a salad
You can eat me with cheese spread
You can sprinkle me with almonds
Then shake sugar on my head
I have travelled here by Eurostar
From somewhere near the Med

Je m'appelle Claude le Croissant
I am neither bun nor cake
Soft and flaky I'm the pastry
That's the tastiest of bakes

Je m'appelle Claude le Croissant
I'm the favoured food of France
Other doughs try to outdo me
But they never stand a chance

You can cover me with butter
You can smother me with jam
You can serve me with a salad
You can fill me up with ham
Your companion from the Continent
Remember who I am

Je m'appelle Claude le Croissant
Star of your patisserie
If you bite me and you like me
Shout out "Oui! Oui! Oui!"

NZ

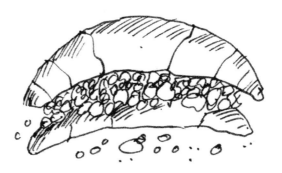

Le Recipe Tip: Cheese Croissant

Take a croissant
Cut it in half
Add cheese*
Eat.
(*Butter optional)

Pizza Delivery Man

Pizza delivery man
Pizza delivery man

I'm the man to bring your pizza
It's my job, it's my career

Pizza delivery man
Pizza delivery man

Mushroom, onion, chicken topping
Ham, tomato, there's no stopping

Pizza delivery man
Pizza delivery man

Mega size with pepperoni
You can order if you phone me

Pizza delivery man
Pizza delivery man

Love to taste that mozzarella?
Look no further I'm your fella

Pizza delivery man
Pizza delivery man

Parsley, basil, oregano
You'll believe you're in Milano

Pizza delivery man
Pizza delivery man

Garlic bread I'm baking also
Pick your dinner from my menu

Pizza delivery man
Pizza delivery man

To your door in half an hour
Brought to you by pizza power

Pizza delivery man
Pizza delivery man

Pizza delivery man
Pizza delivery man

NZ

Dodgy Food Fact

Since 1973 Mrs Jean Okapi of Derbyshire has held the record for
the most number of toppings recorded on a single pizza (47).

The Niciest Spiciest Curry

It's hotter than an oven
or a frying pan.
You can't cool it with water,
you can't cool it with a fan.
Are you a boy
or are you a man?
I tell you, it's not funny –
it's the niciest spiciest curry.

It's hotter than lava,
hotter than the sun.
It'll burn your mouth,
it'll sizzle in your tum.
It'll make you sweat
when it shoots out your bum.
You'll wail for your mummy –
it's the niciest spiciest curry.

It's hotter than a cauldron
full of glowing coals.
It'll make you rock,
it'll make you roll
so get yourself
a steaming bowl
and scoff it in a hurry –
it's the niciest spiciest curry.

It's hotter than an iron
or a red hot flame.
It makes a volcano
look pretty lame.
You'll go insane
and forget your name;
it's brutal, don't you worry –
it's the niciest
   riciest
      diciest
         mightiest
            feistiest
               spiciest
                 CURRY!

JS

Dodgy Food Fact

"Curry" is an ancient Indian word meaning "really really really really really really really really really really really really spicy".

Limerick

There was a young man from Dubai
One morning who started to cry
He was very silly
For while chopping chillies
He got a small piece in his

AAAAIIIIEEEEEEEEEEE!!!!!!!!!

JS

Dodgy Poetry Fact

A limerick is an ancient form of poetry from Madagascar.
It was invented by a lemur called Rick.

Weird

Don't Drink out the Drain

Drinking out the drain
Is not a clever thing to do
'Cause mud and muck and mess and yuck
Combine to brew a stew
You'll end up in the hospital
You'll end up in your bed
It's too impure, there is no cure
At worst you'll end up dead

Drinking out the drain is daft
Don't sip a single drop
Put down the manhole cover now
I'm urging you to stop
Avoid what is disgusting
Full of dark and deadly germs
Inhabited by rats and maggots
Spiders, fleas and worms

Drinking out the drain
Is detrimental to your health
There is no point to quench your thirst
By poisoning yourself
Slurping from a sewage pipe
Is horrible and foul
I'd rather kiss a camel
Or the bottom of a cow

Try a glass of milk instead
A cup of tea or juice
Or water, smoothie, lemonade
There's so much else to choose
You shouldn't take refreshment
From a place of filthy rain
Turn on your tap, it's safer that
You don't drink out the drain

NZ

Dodgy Drain Fact

It is not widely known that the 1912
Olympic Games in Stockholm,
Sweden included a swimming relay
race through the city's sewer system.

Dave's Dad's Eating Dog Food for Dinner

Dave's dad's eating dog food for dinner
Dave's dad's eating dog food for tea
He tells us "Don't waste it
"It's yummy and tasty
"And every dog I know agrees"

Dave's dad's eating dog food in restaurants
Dave's dad's eating dog food in pubs
Wherever the venue
Whatever the menu
He only has one choice of grub

Dave's dad's eating dog food with custard
Dave's dad's eating dog food on toast
When he has this craving
He might pinch the gravy
You're wanting to pour on your roast

Dave's dad's eating dog food with ketchup
Dave's dad's eating dog food with cream
The doctor's remarking
"He's certainly barking
"And now seeing dog food in dreams!"

Dave's dad's eating dog food for supper
Dave's dad's eating dog food for snacks
The dog, starving hungry
Who last ate on Sunday
Is licking his lips at the cat

Dave's dad's eating dog food for breakfast
Dave's dad's eating dog food for lunch
He says "Keep your meat pies
Fruit, salad and French fries
'Cause dog food's the pick of the bunch!"

NZ

Doggy Food Fact

In both written and spoken communication
dogs refer to "dog food" simply as "food".

Rat

What's a nasty thing to eat?
What's a horrid bit of meat?
If a party's full of cheer
what will make the atmosphere
fall flat?

Rat.

What's revolting and abhorrent?
What will make you puke in torrents?
If you served it to your mates
what would cause them all to state
"I'm not eating that"?

Rat.

What's dirty, small and hairy?
What should make you very wary?
If you served it to your boss
what would make him very cross
and hit you with a bat?

Rat.

What's an icky thing to have
when you're sitting in a caff?
What's a most disgusting fare
that will make your friends declare
"I'd rather eat my hat"?

Rat.

What's nice and nutritious?
What's really delicious?
What's a tasty lunch?
What's lovely to munch
(but only if you are a cat)?

RAT!

JS

Dodgy Food Fact

Rat meat tastes like chicken. Go on, try it.

Bacon and an Ice Cube

My dog Winston's favourite meal

I don't want steak
I don't want a bone
I don't want pie
Or an ice-cream cone
I don't want mince
And I don't want chicken
There's only one dish
That I be lickin':

Bacon and an ice cube
Bacon and an ice cube
Bacon and an ice cube
I think it's great
Bacon and an ice cube
Bacon and an ice cube
Bacon and an ice cube
On my plate
Bacon and an ice cube
Bacon and an ice cube
Bacon and an ice cube
When the weather's hot
Bacon and an ice cube
Bacon and an ice cube
Bacon and an ice cube
I like it a lot!

I don't want haddock
Or a leg of lamb
I don't want dog food
From a can
I don't want tripe

And I don't want gravy
There's only one thing
That be drivin' me crazy:

Bacon and an ice cube
Bacon and an ice cube
Bacon and an ice cube
One two three
Bacon and an ice cube
Bacon and an ice cube
Bacon and an ice cube
Just for me
Bacon and an ice cube
Bacon and an ice cube
Bacon and an ice cube
What a treat
Bacon and an ice cube
Bacon and an ice cube
Bacon and an ice cube
Can't be beat!

I don't want leftovers
From your evening meal
I don't want to beg
And I don't want to steal
So I'll sit right here
Just like I should
I know what you'll bring me
If I'm good:

Bacon and an ice cube
Bacon and an ice cube
Bacon and an ice cube
Chew chew chew
Bacon and an ice cube
Bacon and an ice cube
Bacon and an ice cube
Need the loo
Bacon and an ice cube
Bacon and an ice cube
Bacon and an ice cube
Yum yum yum
Bacon and an ice cube
Bacon and an ice cube
Bacon and an ice cube
Out my bum...

...SORRY!

JS

Dodgy Word Fact

In 1998, the word "bum" was voted by children aged 2-7 to be the third funniest word in the world, behind "poop" and "snargle".

Food Bed

Make me a pillow of fluffy marshmallow
Let me lie on a bed of rice
Wrapped in sweet sugar icing sheets
So I'm sandwiched inside snug and nice

I'll wear pyjamas made (of course) from bananas
A sponge cake mattress would be comfy and neat
And if I'm smothered in warm chocolate sauce
I'll sleep for the rest of the week

NZ

Dodgy Food Fact

Food furniture, food transport and even food houses
all became very popular in Japan in the mid-1700s.

Fruit & Veg

Apples

I
like my apples
red. I like my apples
green. But the nicest
apples, they are
somewhere in
between.

JS

Dodgy Poetry Fact

Technically *all* poems are shape poems, but most of them are
just poem-shaped whereas the poem above is apple-shaped.

It's Got to Be a Pea

What is that tiny little ball that's knocking at your door?
Grass-green and round it makes no sound when rolling
   'cross the floor
Born in a pod and served with cod it doesn't grow on trees
It's got to be
It has to be
It's certainly a pea

It might come from a freezer bag or fresh or from a can
It might be liquidised in soup though would taste weird in jam
What's fun to flick at dinnertime at friends or family?
It's got to be
It has to be
It's definitely a pea

It could be minted, split, black-eyed or even marrow fat
Or squished and squashed beneath your shoe, steamrollered,
   fairly flat
Don't stick one up your nostril it will make you sniff and sneeze
It's got to be
It has to be
(The 16th letter of your ABC)
It's unquestionably a pea

NZ

Dodgy Food Fact

At the time of printing this book the total number of peas on
Earth outnumbered the total number of humans by 174.

O, Cauliflower!

O, Cauliflower!
I love you so.
You look like a fantastic flowering fist
punching its way through the earth,
or a cloudy brain brandishing
the soil's sweet secrets.
O, Cauliflower!
Children hate you, and it makes me sad.
I want to gather you in my arms
and feel your charming roughness
against my furrowed cheeks.
I long to feel your wholesome honesty
dance in my nostrils.
I want to scrub my skin with you.
O, Cauliflower!
Your shrubbery
makes my legs
go rubbery.
Please don't ever leaf me!

JS

Dodgy Food Fact

In 1930's Alabama, Reverend Cornelius Buckleberry fought
a well-publicised campaign to legalise human-vegetable
marriages. As of 2017 there have been 320 such marriages,
the latest being between Mississippi resident Bumpkin McGee
and a marrow named Barbara.

Dragon Fruit

Its stalk is a pipeline
to the secrets of history

Its flesh is a swirling
ocean of mystery

Its seeds are the embryos
of faraway moons

Its skin is the silk
of a fire-cocoon

Its taste is the tune
of a never-heard song

Come take a bite with me –
what could go wrong?

JS

Dodgy Food Fact

All the lines in the poem above are the actual, literal truth.

Ba nana nana nana nana nana nana nana nana nana nana nana nana nana

What's the longest fruit you've seen?
Found in milkshake, yoghurt and ice cream
When they're on my plate I lick it clean
A tremendous taste
Too good to waste
Ba nana nana nana nana nana nana nana nana nana nana nana nana nana

You'll slip upon their slimy skin
So put the peel into the bin
What word doesn't stop after it begins?
Simply unending
I'm always bending my
Ba nana nana nana nana nana nana nana nana nana nana nana nana nana

You can mash them
You can squash them
You can squish them
You can gulp them
You can fry them
You can spread them
You can pound them
You can pulp them
When I ask what food you've had today
I'm hoping that you're going to say
Ba nana nana nana nana nana nana nana nana nana nana nana nana nana

Monkeys eat them at the zoo
They're yellow and black not orange and blue
Ideal in soup or in a stew
They're versatile
Shaped like a smile
Ba nana nana nana nana nana nana nana nana nana nana nana nana nana

Buy them by the kilo, pound or bunch
Stick them in your sandwich box for lunch
They're the ideal snack when it comes to the crunch
Travelling all the way from Jamaica
What fruit's got a name that's a record breaker?
Ba nana nana nana nana nana nana nana nana nana nana nana nana nana

Before you get some from the store
Shout out this poem's title once more
Ba nana nana nana nana nana nana nana nana nana nana nana nana nana

NZ

Dodgy Food Fact

The word "banana" was introduced
into the English language by the
Vikings and means "mysterious bent
long yellow black thing".

45

Russell the Brussels Sprout

I'm Russell the Brussels Sprout
A roughy
A toughy
A beast
And a lout
I bully my way onto your plate
I'm rude
I'm crude
I'm the food you most hate
Bad Bill Broccoli is my best mate
I'm Russell the Brussels Sprout

I'm small
So uncool
A poisonous ball
Awfully obnoxious
And not sweet at all
Can you think of a more horrid vegetable
Than me – Russell the Brussels Sprout?

I'll ruin your delicious Christmas dinner
Give you frightening nightmares as well
If you want "disgusting" then I'm a winner
I'm cooked in the kitchens of hell

I'm mean
I'm green
Utterly obscene
You'd prefer a cute carrot or a beautiful bean
Cover me in ketchup
Smother me in sauce
Drown me in gravy
I'll still spoil your main course
If I'm finally swallowed it's often by force
I'm Russell the Brussels Sprout

I'm deadly and foul
I'm putrid and rotten
And bitter – so best left on shop shelves forgotten
I'm the storm cloud to spoil the sunniest day
'Cause I make so much wind that I'll blow you away
All children scream "YUCK" when they see me and say
"I don't want Russell the Brussels Sprout"

NZ

Recipe Tip:
Brussels Sprouts
1. Just Don't!

How to Recreate the Smell of the Durian

Find a herd of buffalo.
Feed them twenty tons of rotten eggs.
Wait until they go to the toilet,
then gather up the dung.
Mix this with mouldy cheddar,
gone-off milk
and your brother's dirty socks (*Mmmmmm!*)
Stuff this into the stomach
of a dead sheep,
then bury it in a pit of maggots.
Leave for a year.
Unearth it, then garnish
with rat's vomit.
Sounds disgusting, yes?

Well it doesn't even come close.

JS

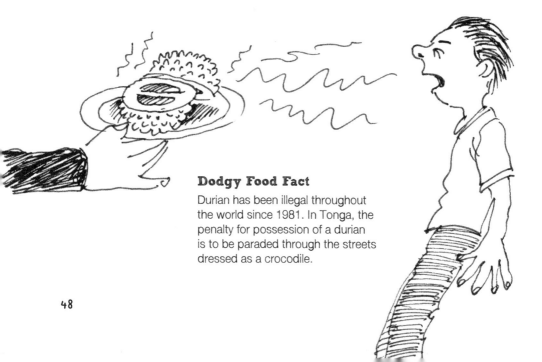

Dodgy Food Fact
Durian has been illegal throughout
the world since 1981. In Tonga, the
penalty for possession of a durian
is to be paraded through the streets
dressed as a crocodile.

On the Side

Kids Love Ketchup

Kids love ketchup on their chips
Kids love ketchup on their crisps
Kids love ketchup on their eggs
Kids love ketchup on their bread

Kids love ketchup on baked beans
And to drown the taste of greens
Kids love ketchup though of course
Posh kids say "tomato sauce"

Kids love ketchup on pork chops
Chicken, chocolate, lollipops
Kids love ketchup they form queues
Just to watch that ketchup ooooooooooze

Kids love ketchup in meat pies
Make my bottle jumbo size
Kids love ketchup on their plates
It's the relish they most rate

Kids love ketchup on their hair
Hands, nose, clothes and everywhere
Kids love ketchup twenty-four seven
Like to live in ketchup heaven

Kids love ketchup on their cheese
Kids love ketchup freshly squeeeeeeeeeezed
Dig the red ketchuppy mess
Do kids love ketchup?
Yes! Yes! Yes!

NZ

Dodgy Food Fact
King Henry VIII so loved tomato ketchup that he
regularly shared a bath of it with one of his many wives.

What a Pickle!

I'm the pickle
in the burger
that is sitting
on your plate,
and I'm proud to
be an item
almost every-
body hates.

I was plucked up
from a hell-hole
where I lay, all
soaked in brine,
by an evil
fast-food worker,
and he sliced me
mighty fine,

then he put me
in a burger
'twixt the patty
and the bap,
and I love to
send the children
into quite a
frightful flap.

When they see me
they're not keen, they
make a heaving,
gagging sound,
then with fingers
pinched like tweezers
plop me down
upon the ground,

where you'll find me
wrapped in napkins,
under tables,
under chairs.
I'm a murky
lurkin' gherkin.
No one likes me.
I don't care.

JS

Dodgy Food Fact

Pickolas Pickleby is another novel by
the famous author Charles Chickens.

By Royal Appointment

Does
the Queen
eat that sticky, black, gooey spread
that goes on bread?

Well,
Ma'am might.

JS

Dodgy Food Fact

She does. Probably.

Jam

Cars, coaches, taxis, trucks
Buses, vans, bikes
Mopeds, lorries, limousines
Ambulances, trikes

What would be tasty with my toast?
Not marmalade, cheese or ham
I thought instead that on the bread
I'd spread some traffic jam

NZ

Dodgy Food Fact

In 1942 Edward Blubber of Adelaide, Australia made a
gooseberry jam so sticky that the saucepan in which it
was cooked stuck to his hand and remained there until
he had it surgically removed 22 years later.

H2O

Water, water everywhere
To wash in and to drink
Filling up the swimming pool, the bath and kitchen sink
It makes the grass and flowers grow
In winter time it's ice and snow
In France it's known as just plain "eau"
Go with the flow
It's H2O

It has no colour, taste or smell
Found in rivers, lakes and wells
Splash, splash, splosh, splosh
Drip, drip, drop, drop
Rain, rain, rain will it ever stop?
Precipitation all over our nation
Go with the flow
It's H2O

Two-thirds of the Earth is covered in it
It's home to billions of fishes
Dangerous enough to drown all of us
Yet without it how would we do the dishes?
Great to shower in
Great to bathe in
Put down that water pistol, stop misbehaving
Go green instead, start water saving
Go with the flow
It's H2O

People die when it runs out
In Africa in times of drought
In the sweltering, scorching, sizzling sun
But if it's plentiful
Like in a waterfall
It's gurgling, gushing, glorious fun
What liquid's top of the plops at number one?
Be saturated not dehydrated
Go with the flow
It's H2O

It's in the waves of the oceans
In the tide of the seas
In the wet of our sweat
And in the "achoooooooooo" of your sneeze
It's in coffee, milkshakes, juice and teas
Turning to steam at one hundred degrees
Though at zero you can watch it freeze
I'm so thirsty, pour me a glass of water please
Go with the flow
It's H2O

NZ

Dodgy Watery Fact

The bottled water we drink comes from the sea so is
originally coloured blue until it is made transparent in
laboratories on islands off the west coast of Scotland.

Weirder

I've Never Eaten a Wozzlenut

I've eaten a mongoose wing pickled in brine
I've sampled the pins of the elephant pine
I've gorged on tarantulas' toenails, but
I've never eaten a wozzlenut.

I've slurped on the pulp of the Antarctic fig
I've tasted the tusks of the great woolly pig
I've munched on the milt of the metalbug, but
I've never eaten a wozzlenut.

I've sipped on the sap of the porcupine plum
I've chewed twenty sticks of Galapagos gum
I've gulped the green milk of the Martian moose, but
I've never eaten a wozzlenut.

I've searched high and low for the rarest of treats
From billiard-bubbles to flying fish feet
But one thing that never has nibbled my nozzle –
The knobbly nut from the wobbly wozzle.

JS

Dodgy Food Fact

Wozzlenuts are native to the country of Dbwpufbwjfbweiufhefwuebf.
They are about the same size as a piece of string, and taste like
light switches, apparently.

The Strangest Fish

The strangest fish on all the planet
You can't fry or smoke or can it
Governments have tried to ban it –
Come and get your
Eeeeeeeeeeeeeeeeeeeeeeeeeeeeeeeeeeeeeeeeeeeeeeeel!

For sheer length you cannot match it
No strength in the world can catch it
Bombs and guns cannot dispatch it –
Come and get your
Eeeeeeeeeeeeeeeeeeeeeeeeeeeeeeeeeeeeeeeeeeeeeeeeeel!

I knew someone who tried to eat it
Took him ages to complete it
(Even longer to excrete it) –
Come and get your
Eeeeeeeeeeeeeeeeeeeeeeeeeeeeeeeeeeeeeeeeeeeeeeeeeel!

Longer than the longest cable
Don't serve it, you won't be able
Leave it off your dinner table –
Do not touch that
Eeeeeeeeeeeeeeeeeeeeeeeeeeeeeeeeeeeeeeeeeeeeeeeeeee
   eeeeeeeeeeeeeeeeeeeeeeeeeeeeeeeeeeeeeeeeeeeeeeeee
   eeeeeeeeeeeeeeeeeeeeeeeeeeel!

JS

Dodgy Food Fact

An eeeeeeeeeeeeeeeeeeeeeeeeeeeeeeeeeeeeeeee
eeeeeeeeeeeeeeeeeeeeeeeeeeeeeeel's favourite food is
banananananananananananananananananananananananananana.

Monster Munch

Half a snikklesnib from Saturn
Plus a pinch of peppered thrag
Mixed with chiffick from Omegon 3
Soaked in thick grolls of grippled zag
Barbecued on fritting floppers
Topped off with poogapeas
In our kitchen there's an alien
Who's insisting on cooking our tea

NZ

Dodgy Food Fact

Many aliens, convincingly disguised as humans, have been
known to present popular cooking shows on UK TV.

Snot: Yuck Version

Snot's not for picking.
No, snot's not.
Snot's not for licking.
No, snot's not.
Snot's not for munching.
No, snot's not.
Snot's not for crunching.
No, snot's not.

Snot: Yum Version

Snot snot for picking!
Nose, snot snot!
Snot snot for licking!
Nose, snot snot!
Snot snot for munching!
Nose, snot snot!
Snot, snot for crunching!
Nose, snot snot!

JS

Dodgy Food Fact

According to scientists, ear wax is
the least tasty bodily mucus.

My Baby Brother

My mum says
my baby brother
is so cute
she wants
to eat him up.

He doesn't seem
very tasty to me.

He smells of
warm milk and sick,
with a side dish
of dirty nappy.

His fingers don't look
nearly as nice
as fish fingers,
or his ears
as sweet
as ears of corn.

I'd rather eat
a chocolate button
than his bellybutton,
and his legs
can't compete
with chicken drumsticks.

My mum says
my baby brother
is so cute
she wants
to eat him up.

I really don't
understand that.

But I suppose, if I had to,
then I'd eat the cat.

JS

Dodgy Food Fact

In Austria in the 1300s, a baby was born so
cute that his mother *did* actually eat him.
With chips.

Snacks

Who Stole the Jam from My Doughnut?

Who stole the jam from my doughnut?
Where did that sweet sticky stuff go?
There ought to be plenty
It's totally empty
Instead of a heart there's a hole

Who stole the jam from my doughnut
And left only air in its place?
No filling's inside it
Did some joker hide it?
I'm missing that strawberry taste

Who stole the jam from my doughnut?
You know it's my favourite part
My teatime is no fun
Since my bun was undone
Did you take it for your jam tart?

Who stole the jam from my doughnut
And gave me a nasty surprise?
Police cars are coming
Those sirens are humming
I'm told it's a serious crime

Who stole the jam from my doughnut
Thus causing such sadness and grief?
Child, teen or a grown-up
Won't somebody own up?
Hands up now if you are the thief!

NZ

Dodgy Food Fact
Until the discus was invented doughnuts were used in
Olympic throwing competitions.

Eat a Peanut

Eat a peanut
Eat a peanut
More a bush and less a tree nut
Sometimes salty like the sea nut
Eat a peanut

Eat a peanut
Eat a peanut
It's an oval in a shell nut
So much simpler to spell nut
Eat a peanut

Eat a peanut
Eat a peanut
Not a Q, R, S or T nut
The as happy as can be nut
Eat a peanut

Eat a peanut
Eat a peanut
Which attracts the highest score nut?
Whether roasted or a raw nut
Eat a peanut

Eat a peanut
Eat a peanut
If you're fancying a snack nut
It's the easiest to crack nut
Eat a peanut

Eat a peanut
Eat a peanut
Mix it up with lots of fruit nut
What's the one that monkeys choose nut?
Eat a peanut

Eat a peanut
Eat a peanut
Eat a peanut

NZ

Nutty Food Fact

The world's largest peanut is approximately four times
bigger than the world's largest elephant.

Something in My Sandwich!

breadbreadbreadbreadbreadbreadbreadbread

tomatolettucetomatolettucetomatolettuce

cucumbercucumbercucumbercucumber

mustardketchupmayomustardketchupmayo

beefbeefbeefbeefbeefbeeftoenailbeefbeef

butterbutterbutterbutterbutterbutterbutter

breadbreadbreadbreadbreadbreadbreadbread

JS

Dodgy Food Fact

In 2015 Bleston Humenthal unveiled the bread sandwich –
a piece of bread between two slices of bread.

Daddy's Burnt the Toast!

When Daddy cooks he's bound to fail.
He tries his best, to no avail.
The neighbours scream, the sirens wail
when Daddy burns the toast.

His flailing arms are not a joke.
We splutter on the acrid smoke.
Oh what a careless, silly bloke —
Daddy's burnt the toast!

He feels unappreciated,
dismal and humiliated.
Breakfast? It has been cremated —
Daddy's burnt the toast!

We're sorry Dad, we think you're brill
despite your monstrous lack of skill.
We want to say we love you still,
but please don't burn the toast!

JS

Dodgy Food Fact

The Great Fire of London began
when someone burnt the toast.

Sweets

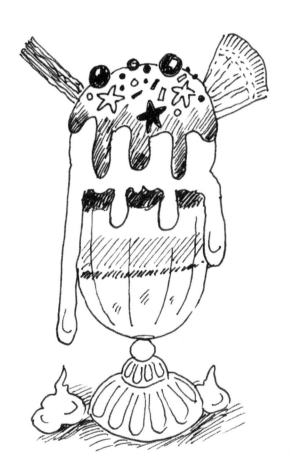

Brainfreeeeeeeeze!

Your noggin's been hit by a runaway train
Your eyes both water and you're in great pain
You're an ice cream addict but you must complain
Turn the heating up please
It's brainfreeeeeeeeze!

Though you've only put two scoops in your bowl
There's a hammering hard inside your skull
Yet you torture yourself with this huge own goal
Every doctor agrees
It's brainfreeeeeeeeze!

As another ice age forms in your head
You ignore all the signs that are flashing red
You refuse to play safe eating cake instead
Weak wobbly knees
It's brainfreeeeeeeeze!

Many times more nasty than a dentist's drill
Such a cold sugar rush giving you a big thrill
Even on summer days you will shiver and chill
Worse than smelly blue cheese
Minus forty degrees
It's a subarctic breeze
Makes a polar bear sneeze
It's brainfreeeeeeeeze!

NZ

Dodgy Food Fact

A brontosaurus was recently found in Canada whose body had been perfectly preserved for millions of years in peach and mango ice cream.

Short & Sweet

Jelly baby!
Jelly baby! Jelly baby!
Jelly baby! Jelly baby!
Jelly baby!
Jelly baby!

Eat the arms, then the legs
Then the body, then the head

Jelly baby! Jelly baby!
Jelly baby!
Jelly baby!
Jelly baby!
Jelly baby!
Jelly baby!

NZ

Dodgy Food Fact

Before jelly was invented jelly babies used to be made of wood
although, quite prophetically, they were still called jelly babies.

Life is Better with a Cake

Life is better with a cake
You can't beat a sticky bun
Danish pastry, Black Forest gateau
Battenberg, Victoria sponge
Choose a food that's fun, fun, fun
Mix flour, egg, sugar, butter etcetera
What's it going to make?
That tantalising treasure
That gorgeous guilty pleasure
Life is better with a cake

Chocolate eclair, treacle tart
Fudge brownie, apple strudel
Where to start?
Indulge your cup of tea or coffee
With a wedge of fresh banoffee
Sprinkled with crushed almond flakes
A double-sized slice
Is twice as nice
Life is better with a cake

I hang around the bakery
I lurk in the patisserie
No longer counting calories
There's only one dessert for me
Dripping raspberry sauce
Oozing jam and double cream
Packaged like a perfect dream
Madeira, red velvet, New York cheese
Tiramisu, Swiss roll, Dundee
Yes please!
While you go weak at the knees you know
That comfy, warm internal glow
Life is better with a cake

So when everything stops
At eleven o'clock
Celebrate today with a cherry on top
No need to slobber for a steak
For your satisfaction's sake
Brighten up your morning break
By eating as much of that sweet stuff
As your appetite can take
Life is better with a cake

NZ

Dodgy Food Fact

The first ever birthday cake was baked in 3287 BCE
and consisted mainly of rocks, mud and grass.

My Secret Chocolate Stash

I've got a secret chocolate stash
That's hidden in my house
It's stored securely somewhere safe
For when my sweets run out

It's buried under lock and key
And is completely mine
A scrumptious bar of heaven
My emergency supply

And if today is grim and grey
With rain instead of sun
I'll bolt my door, sit on my floor
Then stuff my face for fun

I know it isn't healthy
I know it isn't right
But I just can't resist a food
So beautiful to bite

Twelve perfect squares to savour
Gobble, nibble, nosh and pick
I don't care I've eaten dinner
And am feeling sick

Who is the one to turn to
When I am feeling down?
My friendly, fatty, sugary mate
Delicious, smooth and brown

You can turn my bedroom inside out
Until it's totally trashed
Still you'll never, ever, ever, ever, ever find...
My secret chocolate stash

NZ

Extremely Dodgy Food Fact

When a thousand children were surveyed, 99.4 % of them
said they would prefer Brussels sprouts to chocolate if
they had to choose one or the other for a snack.

Custard Man

I'm Custard Man
Give me custard, man
On pudding, on pie, on fruit, on flan
Banana flavour, vanilla or chocolate
Serve me some I'll slurp the lot of it
Strawberry sauce or raspberry jam
Don't fit in with my master plan
All I desire is custard, man

I love it in a can or tin
I love it when it's runny thin
I love it so much it's a sin
I'd even drink it from your bin

I'm Custard Man
Give me custard, man
On pork, on peas, on lettuce, on lamb
If I found four bowls of blancmange
I'd soak them up just like a sponge
Once my meals were dull and bland
Now I'm this liquid's biggest fan
I want to live in Custardland

I love it whether cold or hot
I love it with the skin on top
I love it so much I can't stop
Until I taste the final drop

I'm Custard Man
Give me custard, man
On spaghetti, on stew, on haddock, on ham
I hate hot dogs smothered in mustard
My rule is it's cool to be caked in custard
None of my friends can understand
They say my craving's out of hand
But I reply "More custard, man!"

I love it when it's set and thick
I always love to have a lick
I love it till I'm feeling sick
This habit is too hard to kick

Why scream for ice cream
When it isn't my scene
And only one thing
Fulfils my dreams?
For starter, sweet and in-between
I'm a fellow liking yellow
Not red or blue or green
I'm Custard Man
I'm the Custard King
Give me custard, custard, custard!

NZ

Dodgy Food Fact
Custard is the favourite food of camels but extremely few people
are aware of this as camels are so rarely offered custard.

Gluttony

Man vs Food

The hottest stew, the biggest steak
The largest pizza you can make
A breakfast made with twenty eggs
A bowl of spicy chicken legs
Six litres of the strongest beer –
He'll do it all, he has no fear!

The hugest ever apple pie
He doesn't even need to try
Nine dozen oysters from their shells
Ghost chillies from the depths of hell
A jumbo plate of spicy rib –
All he needs is one clean bib!

Meals made of twenty courses
Burgers made from dogs and horses –
He's the champ, he is the best
But this man needs a proper test,
A dish to make him squirm and cower:
My mum's boiled cauliflower.

JS

Dodgy Food Fact

American ornithologist Hank Bont holds the record for the
most grains of sugar consumed in an hour (twelve million).

Charlie the Chipetarian

Laura was a librarian
Suzy a Sagittarian
Reggie a Rastafarian
But Charlie
Was a chipetarian

Chips were the only food he'd eat
No salad
No fruit
No veg
No fish
And definitely no meat
He was chock-a-block with chips from his head
    down to his feet
He'd salivate and lick his lips
At the thought of piles and piles of chips

People said
"You'll turn into a French fry
You'll turn into a spud"
He had a litre of chip fat
Coursing through his blood
And once he'd finished his chip supper
What would be his snack for later?
He had no doubt about his choice
Another chipped potato

He was full of chips to the brim
Not enough
Green stuff
Or vitamins
Went into him

'Cause he ate
And ate
And ate
And ate
The mountains of chips stacked up on his plate

His mum said he'd never live to twenty
(Never mind make an octogenarian)
If he stuck with his decision
To be a chipetarian
The staff mistook him for a whale
At the local aquarium
He was so overweight
He couldn't get a date
He accidentally squashed eleven of his mates
When the lake froze over in winter
He was not allowed to skate
The fire brigade had to cut him free
From his front garden gate

But he remained a devout follower
Of the chipetarian cause
Shovelling more chips inside him
Without a moment's pause
Scales strained and broke due to his size
As he changed into a giant chip
Before his family's eyes

It was all rather strange
It was all rather weird
Till finally disaster struck
As everyone had feared

Last Monday he came home
Peckish after school
He ate a single chip then said
"I'm feeling pretty full"
Then came a loud BOOM and BANG
And BANG and BOOM
Charlie was in smithereens
All over his living room

The moral of this story
Is clear for all to see
If you don't want size two hundred hips
If you don't want to bust your zips
If you don't want to be blown to bits
Then follow this advice from me
Chips are fine
Some of the time
But not for breakfast
Lunch
Dinner
And tea

Laura was a librarian
Suzy a Sagittarian
Reggie a Rastafarian
But Charlie
Was a chipetarian

NZ

Recipe Tip: Raw Chips

Although totally tasteless and inedible, these are fat-free,
healthier alternatives to regular chips.

Don't Eat out the Bin!

Don't eat out the bin, dude.
Don't eat out the bin.
Don't make a meal
of old orange peel.
Don't eat out the bin.

Don't eat out the bin, man.
Don't eat out the bin.
Don't nibble and munch
on yesterday's lunch.
Don't eat out the bin.

Don't eat out the bin, bro.
Don't eat out the bin.
Don't be in denial,
it's vulgar and vile.
Don't eat out the bin.

Don't eat out the bin, mate.
Don't eat out the bin.
It's crawling with germs,
and maggots and worms.
Don't eat out the bin.

Don't eat out the bin, pal.
Don't eat out the bin.
Don't gobble and chew
on festering stew.
You make think it's cool
but you are a fool.
You may think it's quirky
but really it's dirty,
so DON'T EAT OUT THE BIN!

JS

Dodgy Recipe: Bin Stew

Throw your meal in the bin
Leave it for a week
Take it out
Eat it with a large spoon.

Bolognese Baby

He's scoffing the lot
Fingers in the pot
Mixed with drips of dribble and drops of snot
Table manners have gone
Self-respect is shot
He's a Bolognese Baby

Sauce in every place
And spaghetti face
No scarier creature's in outer space
Once was sweet and cute
What a fall from grace
He's a Bolognese Baby

He is only three
So when eating tea
Treats a meal as a play activity
Splattering the walls
And mum's new settee
He's a Bolognese Baby

Nobody's impressed
At his filthy mess
When will he learn using a plate is best?
Throw him in the bath
Although he's still dressed
He's a Bolognese Baby

He's filled the floor
Cries out "More! More! More!"
Won't somebody tell him what his fork is for?
Looking like the victim
In a food fight war
We all know the score
He's a Bolognese Baby

NZ

Dodgy Food Fact

The world's shortest piece of spaghetti is 0.000031mm long and
was found in a meal served in a Venezuelan restaurant in 1859.

Yuck   Yum

To order your next main course . . .

www.cccpworkshops.co.uk

www.joshuaseigal.co.uk

www.troikabooks.com